C000126770

Julia Donaldson

Hamlet
the Prince of Denmark

The Queen
Hamlet's mother

The King
Hamlet's uncle

Horatio
Hamlet's friend

Hamlet's father
(a ghost)

Ophelia
Hamlet's girlfriend

Polonius
Ophelia's father

Laertes
Ophelia's brother

It was true. Hamlet's father, the King of Denmark, had died. People said he had been bitten by a snake. Hamlet was away at university when it happened. When he came home for the funeral he didn't like the way his mother always seemed to be crying in his uncle's arms. And now - only two months later - the two of them were married.

That night Hamlet went with Horatio to the battlements. The wind was cold and the moon hid behind a cloud. Hamlet shivered in the black night.

The ghost vanished, and Hamlet made Horatio promise not to tell anyone what had happened.
After that night the world seemed blacker than ever to Hamlet. And yet he couldn't be sure that his uncle was really a murderer. He wanted more proof.

I don't want anyone to know that I suspect the King. If I seem to be a bit mad, then no one will know what I'm really thinking.

Hamlet started acting very strangely. He hardly slept and he hardly ate. His clothes were always in a mess. His behaviour puzzled his girlfriend Ophelia. One day he went into her room, held her face and stared into her eyes without saying anything. Another time he was rude to her father, Polonius.

Polonius, the Prime Minister, had his own ideas about Hamlet. Polonius was a fussy old man who wanted to control Ophelia's life. He had made her send back all Hamlet's letters telling her that Hamlet didn't really love her. But now Polonius had changed his mind. He told the King what he thought.

I know what's driving Hamlet mad. It's his love for my daughter. Let's spy on them and find out more.

Ophelia felt bad about tricking Hamlet and she blushed when she saw him. When Hamlet saw this he grew suspicious. He had already guessed that his two old friends were the King's spies. Now he guessed that there were more spies around. Worse still, Ophelia seemed to be part of this spy ring!

I loved you once.

I thought so.

The King was really worried now. What was the reason for Hamlet's strange behaviour? Could he have found out the King's secret?

As for Hamlet, he sometimes wished he could die. He hated this world of lies and murder. He hadn't forgotten that he had promised to murder his uncle, and yet he couldn't make himself do it. He told himself that he still needed more proof.

The day of the play arrived. Hamlet and his friend Horatio watched the King closely. At first he was smiling. But when the baddie in the play poured poison into his brother's ear, the King's smile turned to a frown. He stood up.

But the angry King stormed out of the room.

Hamlet slipped out after him, his sword in his hand.

Hamlet pulled the curtain back, hoping to see his uncle's body. But there, in a pool of blood, lay Ophelia's father.

This is your fault! How could you forget Dad and marry his wicked brother?

While Hamlet was on his way to England, another young man was on his way to Denmark. It was Ophelia's brother, Laertes. He had been living in France, but when he heard about his father's death he came home. Mad with anger, he burst into the castle.

You killed my father!

No, no, it wasn't me - it was Hamlet!

At that moment, Ophelia wandered in with a bunch of flowers. She had a strange, empty look in her eyes. She started to give the flowers away, talking and singing all the time. Her father's death had been too much for her and she had gone mad. Still talking nonsense, she wandered out again.

The pirates had captured Hamlet, and the two spies had sailed on to England without him. Hamlet had made friends with the pirates and they had taken him back to Denmark. He would soon be home in the castle.
This was bad news for the King. He would have to get rid of Hamlet another way.

Swords in fencing matches were supposed to be blunt.
But the King and Laertes decided to sharpen one of the
swords and dip it in poison ...
Just in case this didn't work, the King would have a
special drink ready - a drink of poison.

On his way home, Hamlet saw a grave being dug. He didn't know who it was for. But then he saw a funeral procession and heard Laertes shouting wildly.

My sister! My poor dead sister!

So Ophelia was dead!

Back in the castle, Hamlet told Horatio what had happened at sea.

I knew my two friends were really the King's spies. So when they were asleep I read the letter he had given them. It said I was to be put to death! I didn't like the sound of that, so I swapped it for another one. Now the two of them will be put to death instead of me!

Hamlet laughed but Horatio shook his head. Where would all this end?

A servant arrived with a message for Hamlet.

Laertes wants you to fence with him.

I agree.

Hamlet was sorry about the fight with Laertes. A friendly fencing match would be a good way to make up with him.

41

The fencing match was in the hall of the castle. Horatio sat down to watch with the King and Queen.

43

The two men began to fight. At first Hamlet was getting the better of Laertes. But then Laertes stabbed Hamlet's arm. Hamlet was shocked to see blood. The swords were supposed to be blunt!

Full of anger, Hamlet knocked the sword out of Laertes's hand. He picked it up and gave Laertes his own sword. Within seconds he had wounded Laertes.

But he was too late. The Queen had drunk the poison.

Laertes's anger against Hamlet melted away. He told him about the poisoned sword and begged to be forgiven.

You and I are both dying, Hamlet.

If I am dying, the King must not live!

Hamlet rushed at the King and stabbed him with the poisoned sword. Then he picked up the poisoned drink and forced it into the King's mouth.

At last the King was dead. At last Hamlet's father could rest in peace. Hamlet had one dying wish.

Horatio, my friend, you alone will be left alive. I want you to tell the world the truth about Hamlet, the Prince of Denmark!